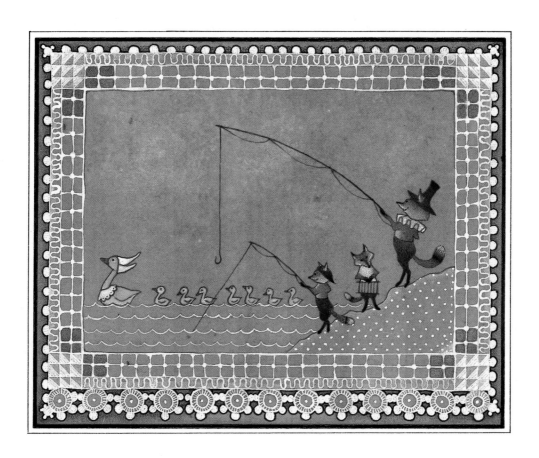

MOTHER GOOSE
and the SLY FOX

Retold and with pictures by

Chris Conover

Farrar, Straus and Giroux

New York

Copyright © 1989 by Chris Conover
All rights reserved
Library of Congress catalog card number: 89-45502
Published in Canada by HarperCollinsCanadaLtd
Color separations by Offset Separations Corp.
Printed and bound in the United States of America
by Horowitz/Rae Book Manufacturers
Designed by Cynthia Krupat
First edition, 1989
Second printing, 1991

For Michael and Caryn

Once there was a Mother Goose who lived in a snug little house. She was always busy, with seven tiny goslings to take care of, and a do-nothing mouse who lived in the wall.

Nearby in a dirty, crooked house there lived a sly fox and his two cubs.

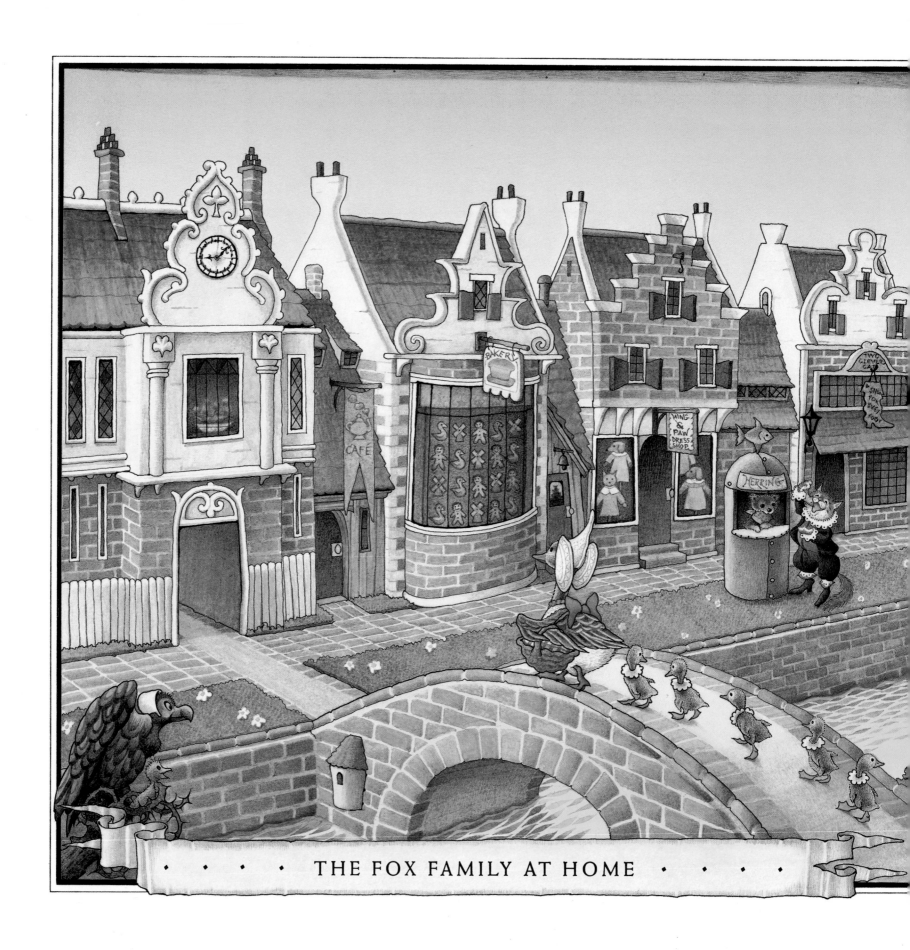

THE FOX FAMILY AT HOME

One morning, Mother Goose got up early. She bustled around the kitchen while her family slept. When breakfast was ready, they tumbled in, each grumpier than the last.

"It's too hot today," whispered one gosling.

"No, too cold!" whined another.

"Our bed is too lumpy," whimpered a third.

"No, too soft!" worried the fourth.

"I want porridge for breakfast," warbled the fifth.

"No. Pancakes!" weaseled the sixth.

The seventh gosling crumbled her toast, and Mr. Mouse didn't help at all.

After breakfast, Mother Goose washed and swept while her children gabbled and grouched. Then she said, "Mr. Mouse, I must go to the market. Will you watch my little ones? And please be very sure they don't let strangers in the house."

Mr. Mouse agreed, and out she went.

Over at Fox's house, the greedy cubs were still hungry, even though they were licking up the remains of a breakfast feast.

"We've had only one duck to eat today," yowled one.

"And only two chickens yesterday," howled the other.

"There goes Mother Goose," Fox said. "Those fat goslings of hers would make a delicious dinner."

"And don't forget that mouse, for dessert!" yipped the cubs.

Fox went to Mother Goose's house and knocked on the door. He growled in his rough, gruff voice, "Let me in, let me in, sweetiekins, it's your dear mother!"

"You don't sound like our mother!" the goslings cried, and they didn't let him in.

Fox went to the miller and bought a sack of flour.

He dabbed some on his tongue, which made his voice soft and smooth.

· FOX HAS A PLAN ·

Then he returned to Mother Goose's house.

"Let me in, my precious ones!" he crooned.

But he put his paw on the windowsill, and his dirty feet showed under the door.

"You don't look like our mother," said the goslings, and they didn't let him in.

This time, Fox went to the baker.

"I've hurt my paw," he lied. "Put some dough on it, will you?"

The kindly baker wrapped his paw in gingerbread.

His next stop was the cobbler's, where he tried on some new shoes. The cobbler took one look at Fox and shook his head. "You're up to some trick, Fox. I won't sell you those shoes."

"If you don't, I'll eat you up," Fox snarled, and marched away in his new shoes.

· · FOX IN DISGUISE ·

For the third time, Fox knocked on Mother Goose's door.

"Let me in, let me in, children. I've brought you presents."

"Presents!" squealed the goslings. "That sounds like Mother!"

They looked at Fox's gingerbread paw draped on the window ledge.

"That looks like Mother," they agreed.

Mr. Mouse glanced under the door and saw large red feet.

"Oh, that's your mother, all right," he said. "No problem."

So the foolish goslings opened the door.

Fox rushed in. He scooped up Mr. Mouse and threw him in the flour sack. He caught the goslings one by one, except for the seventh, who hid in the clock case. Satisfied with his catch, Fox tied the sack tightly and left by the back door.

The noon sun shone hot and bright. His bundle seemed to grow heavier as he trudged along, and he thought, "A quick rest would do me good." Fox stretched out under a shady bush. Soon he was fast asleep.

· SWEET DREAMS, FOX ·

When Mother Goose returned home, she found the door open and her family gone. The seventh gosling jumped out of the clock case and told her the whole terrible story. They rushed out to look for Fox, following his trail until they found him and the bag of wriggling goslings. Mother Goose took out her sharp little scissors and snip, snip, snip! cut a hole in the bag.

"Hush! darlings, hush!" she said as they popped out. "Quickly, find a stone the same size you are and roll it back to me."

While they did that, Mother Goose threaded her needle and the seventh gosling knotted the thread. She put the stones into the sack and sewed it up neatly so no one could tell the difference. Quickly, quietly, she led her goslings home.

· · SHHH! · ·

By and by, Fox awoke with a yawn and a stretch. He looked at the sack lying beside him and smiled. "I'm such a clever fellow!" he thought. "I know just how to get things done!" He picked up the sack and wound the cord around his paw for a good grip and started for home. Crossing the bridge, he said to himself, "These goslings weigh a ton! Well, the fatter the better. We'll have a feast!" And he licked his chops. "A drink would do me good."

He clambered down to the river's edge. As he leaned over to lap some water, the heavy sack pulled him forward. Kersplash! into the river went the sly fox. Weighed down by the stones, he sank straight to the muddy bottom. Three big fish swam over to get a good look. One nipped his nose, another bit his toes, and the third nibbled his tail. Terrified, Fox struggled free, splashing and sputtering. He galloped away as fast as he could, with his two cubs right behind. They fled deep into the forest and were never seen again.

Mother Goose, back home with her family, gave Mr. Mouse a good talking-to.

"How could you be so careless with my babies?" she scolded.

Mr. Mouse was very sorry, and to make up and show that he could do things right, he fixed a delicious supper. Then the goslings cleaned up all by themselves.

And Mother Goose sat in her big comfy chair and had a holiday!

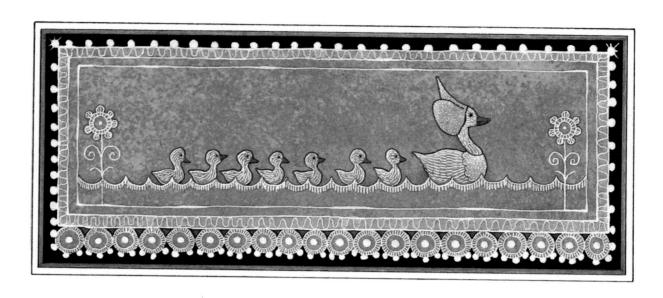

Can you find these characters?

The Little Red Hen
The Three Billy Goats Gruff
Cerberus
The Hare and the Tortoise
Snow White and Rose Red
Unicorn
The Three Bears
Puss in Boots
Chicken Little
Hans the Hedgehog
King Stork
Pegasus
The Three Little Pigs
Mother Goose and the Sly Fox
The Ugly Duckling
The Bremen Town Musicians

FINISH